OUT OF THIN AIR
A Story of Big Trees

By Nancy Muleady-Mecham

Illustrations by Robert E. Muleady
Design by Sandra Kim Muleady

VTP
Vishnu Temple Press • Flagstaff, AZ

ISBN 978-0-9795055-3-9
Library of Congress Control Number: 2009925764

Author photograph, page 43: Sean Brady
Illustrations by Robert E. Muleady
Cover design and book layout: Sandra Kim Muleady

Vishnu Temple Press, LLC
P.O. Box 30821
Flagstaff, AZ 86003-0821
www.vishnutemplepress.com

First Printing, May 2009

PRINTED IN THE UNITED STATES OF AMERICA

ACKNOWLEDGEMENTS

I would like to thank Mary Anne Carlton, Wendy Harrison, Steven K. Stocking, Karyn Shinkle and her marvelous brood of young readers, Tami Rukstad-Schaner, Hazel Clark, Kent Mecham and my family and parents. Working with Bobby and Sandy was a joy.

"Excuse us, Ranger Eileen, can you tell us where the tunnels are that the trees have made?" asked Hope and Timmy.

"Oh, you must mean the Wawona Tunnel Tree in Yosemite National Park," said Ranger Eileen. "That tree had a tunnel cut through it in 1881. The tunnel was so big, buggies pulled by horses and, later, cars could drive through the tree. Unfortunately, this man-made tunnel weakened the tree and it fell down in 1969. There is a similar tunnel tree in Calaveras Big Trees State Park."

"No," said Hope, "not the Wawona Tree. I mean the
tunnel from the trees in the sequoia groves."

"Well, Sequoia National Park has a giant sequoia that fell down on the road to Crescent Meadow in 1937. A tunnel was cut so cars could drive through. It is called Tunnel Log," explained Ranger Eileen.

"Or perhaps you are referring to the giant sequoia in which *Hale Tharp* made his home in Log Meadow," she continued. "It was tunneled out by natural fire and Hale used it as his summer home while he herded cattle in the meadow over one hundred years ago."

Hope shook her head. "No, I mean what happened to the tunnels that all of these trees came from? If trees are growing from the ground, where are the holes, tunnels and ditches that were made when the tree grew? If a tree uses dirt to grow big, shouldn't as much of the dirt be gone as a tree is big?"

"That is a great question, Hope. Let's join Timmy and
I will tell you how trees come mostly from the air!"

"Dirt is very important to a tree," Ranger Eileen began. "We call it soil. It has very important *nutrients* that allow the tree to grow. The most important is nitrogen.

"Nitrogen is an element. Elements are made of atoms and can combine with other elements to make *molecules.* If we took all the parts that make up things and looked at the smallest building blocks, we would see the elements. There are 103 natural elements. Each of these is unique and has special properties."

Periodic Table of Elements

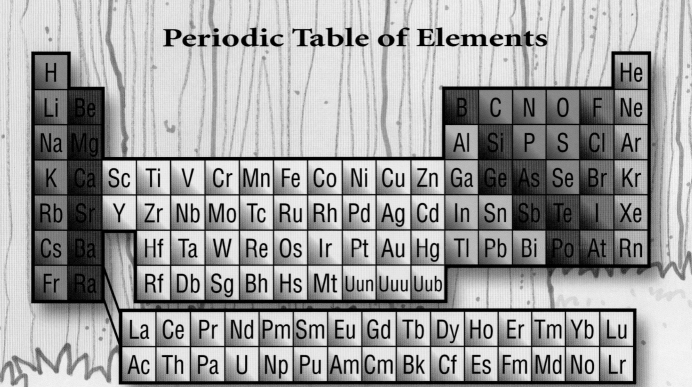

"Oxygen is an element," continued Ranger Eileen. "It has a special property of being a gas at room temperature. We can breathe it into our lungs where it is used to keep us alive by providing fuel to process the food we eat."

"The element hydrogen is also a gas, but it is smaller than oxygen and burns easily. It is the hydrogen burning in our sun that gives us the light we see in the daytime.

"And it is this sunlight that the moon reflects to us at nighttime, like a big mirror."

"Carbon is also an element. It is the building block of all living things here on earth. Anything that is living and made of carbon is called *organic*. While there is carbon in the soil, a lot of it is in our air also."

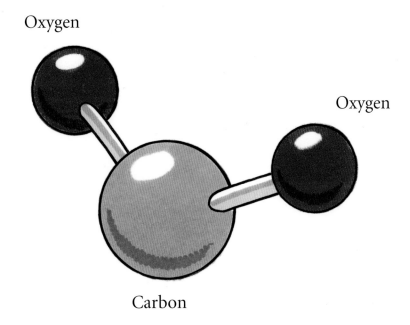

Oxygen

Oxygen

Carbon

"Carbon in the air can be mixed with the gas, oxygen. There are two oxygen atoms for every carbon atom. Even though carbon is not always a gas, when it meets two oxygen molecules it is able to float. We call this new gas *carbon dioxide*," Ranger Eileen explained.

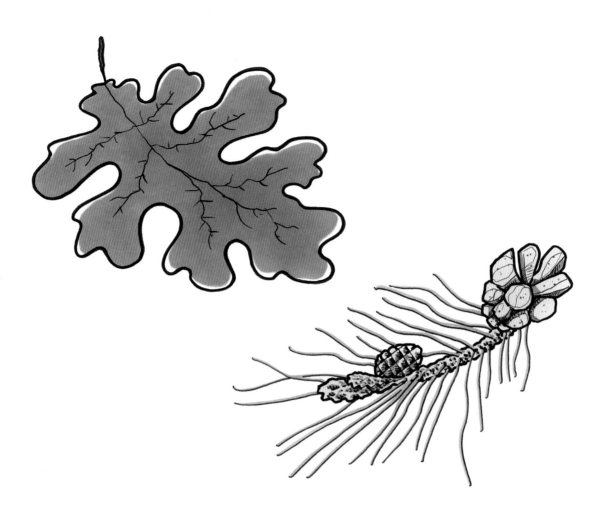

"Leaves on trees come in many shapes. They can be big like the oak trees or thin like the needles on pine trees and giant sequoias." Ranger Eileen smiled. "Think of needles as just skinny leaves!"

"Trees with needles are adapted to snowy winters. We see these in all of the giant sequoias, from Sequoia National Park to Calaveras Big Trees State Park."

Ranger Eileen continued to explain, "Thin needles prevent a lot of snow from settling on them. The sloping branches of the tree cause the snow that does land to fall off so the branches don't break from the weight of the snow."

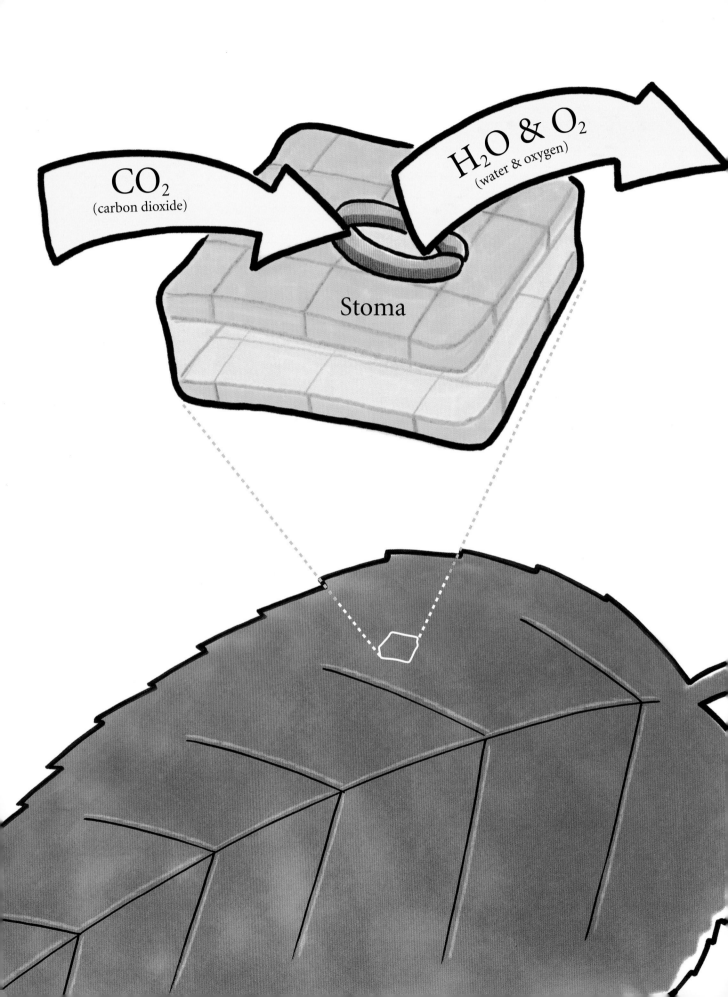

"Leaves have special tiny doorways in them called *stoma*. When the stoma are open, carbon dioxide from the air can go inside the leaf. The leaves use the sun's energy, plus carbon dioxide and other elements, to make sugars in a process called *photosynthesis*.

"Sugars are a type of *carbohydrate*. The word is formed from:

> *carb* for carbon
> *o* for oxygen
> *hydrate* for water.

"Many molecules that make a tree contain the element carbon. Carbon helps to make sugars, sap, branches, cones, seeds, *bark,* and the wood of a tree."

"Most trees are made of about 50% carbon from the carbon dioxide they get from the air. The element oxygen is returned to the air after the carbon is used to make the tree. That is why it is important to have lots of healthy plants on earth because they provide us with the oxygen animals and people breathe to stay alive."

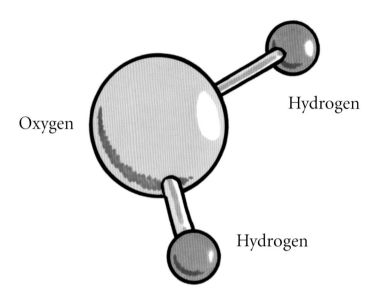

Oxygen

Hydrogen

Hydrogen

"When we look at a piece of wood, a lot of that wood is made of water. Water has two hydrogen atoms and one oxygen atom.

"At room temperature, we know that water is liquid, but when you get it hot, it becomes a gas we call steam.

"That is what you see when you burn wood in a campfire – the steam of the water in the wood rising. When the steam has particles of burning wood in it, like ash, it becomes darker and we call it smoke. The amount of water in the wood can change as the wood dries."

25

"The wood of a giant sequoia is mostly carbon and water. *Only a few elements come from the soil!*

Hope and Timmy looked at the trees with more interest now.

Ranger Eileen continued, "Water carries nutrients from the ground up to the needles in the tree. With these nutrients, needles make sugars which travel back to the roots and other parts of the tree in the sap.

"In maple trees, the sap is very sweet. We make syrup from the maple's sap."

"Water and a tree's sap travel in layers made by the living part of the tree called the *cambium*. This layer lies under the bark and outside the wood of the tree. Every year the cambium adds a new layer of bark and a new layer of wood. After a few years, those new layers become bark and wood and are no longer alive."

"So most of the trunk part of the tree is dead?!" exclaimed Timmy.

"Yes," smiled Ranger Eileen, "but the wood gives the tree strength and the bark protects the cambium like skin on you and me."

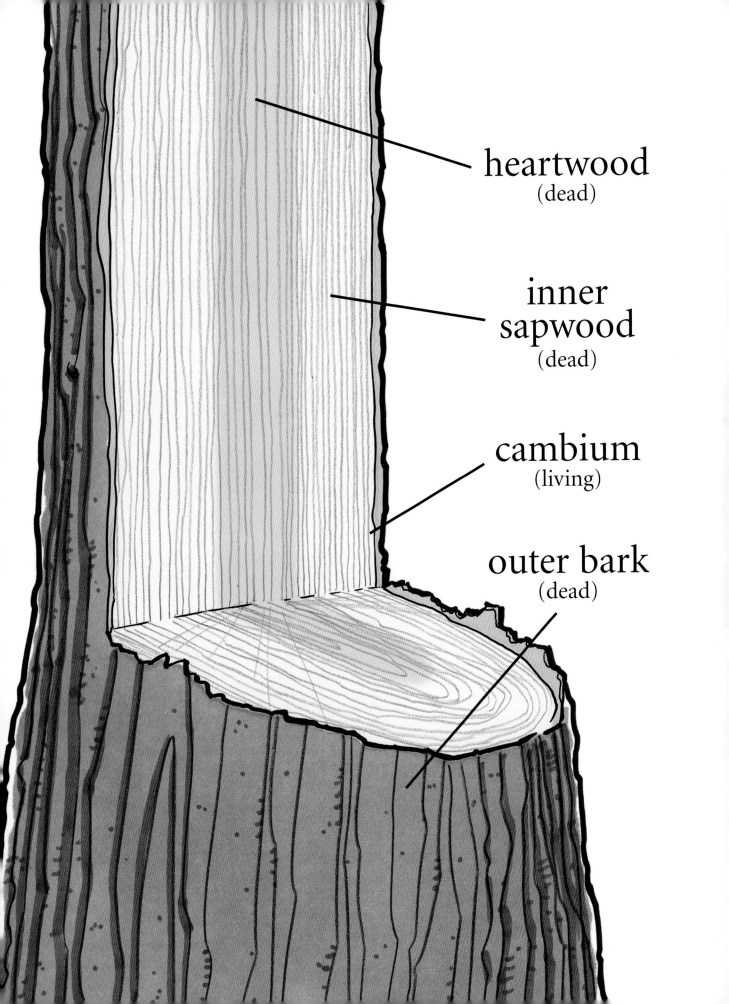

heartwood
(dead)

inner
sapwood
(dead)

cambium
(living)

outer bark
(dead)

Ranger Eileen continued, "While a tree is alive, it holds a lot of water and a lot of carbon. Can you imagine how much carbon is in an entire forest? In the ancient past, when forests of trees and other organic life died and became buried, the carbon eventually became the carbon in coal, oil and natural gas. There is only a limited supply of these *carbon-based energy sources.*"

"Today, when trees are cut down in large numbers, there is more carbon in the *atmosphere*. Fewer trees mean less carbon is taken out of the air.

Many scientists believe that this increase of carbon dioxide is trapping heat in our atmosphere, contributing to an increase in temperature throughout the world. This is called *global warming*. Many scientists believe this warming will cause changes in the weather throughout the planet!"

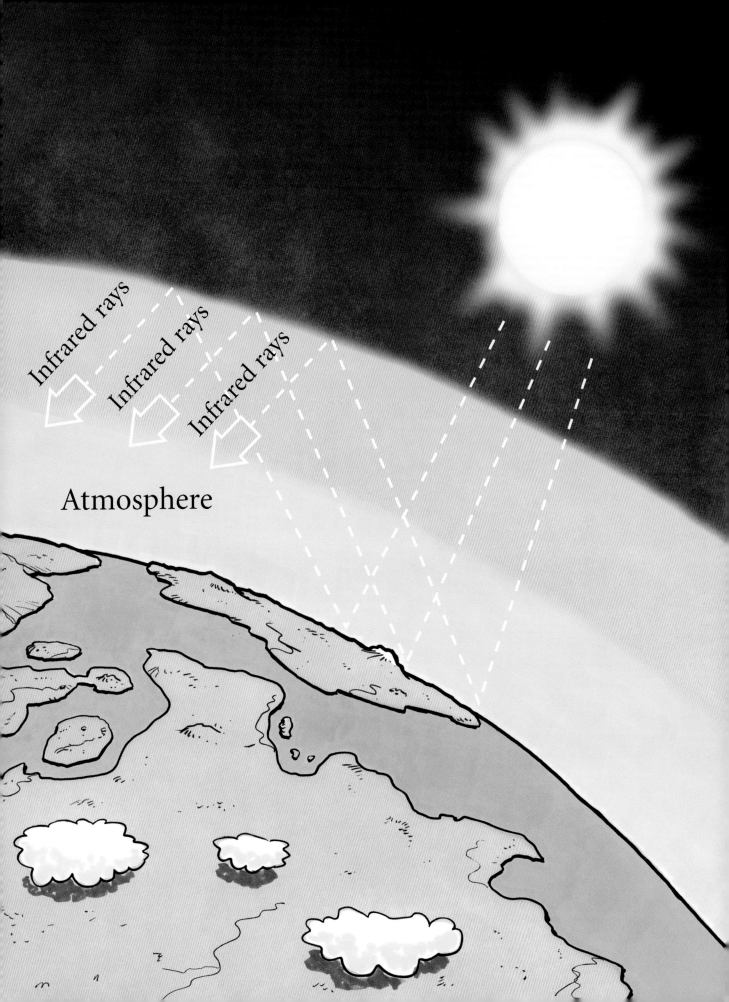

"Here in a grove of giant sequoias, we are high in elevation. Giant sequoias grow in groves from 4,000 feet to over 8,000 feet above sea level! There is less *pressure* this high and the air thins."

Ranger Eileen asked, "Did you notice how your bag of marshmallows expanded as you drove up into the mountains?"

Hope and Timmy nodded.

Ranger Eileen concluded, "So you see, Hope and Timmy, there are no ditches or tunnels or holes because only a tiny bit of dirt is needed to provide nutrients to a tree. A lot of what makes a tree a tree comes from the air. And because the air in the mountains is thinner than the air at sea level, you can say that the trees are made out of thin air!"

GLOSSARY

atmosphere – the area above the earth's surface that contains molecules of the air and other elements, usually as gases.

bark – the outer layer of a tree that protects the tree.

cambium – the living layer of a tree between the bark and wood. Cambium makes a new layer of wood and bark every year.

carbohydrate – a molecule made of carbon, oxygen and water. It is a basic building and food molecule for life.

carbon-based energy sources – molecules that contain carbon and usually hydrogen; can be newly-formed like methane, or old from fossils, like oil and natural gas. They can provide heat and energy when burned.

carbon dioxide – a molecule that contains one atom of carbon and two atoms of oxygen. It is a gas that makes up part of our atmosphere and is an important building molecule for trees.

global warming – the trend of planet earth to increase its average temperature over time. This is due in part to more molecules in the atmosphere that are able to hold heat. With fewer trees to hold carbon, more carbon as carbon dioxide contributes to global warming. This can then cause global climate changes.

heartwood – the inner core of the trunk that gives the tree strength and stability. It is dead wood produced by the *cambium (see above)*.

infrared rays – invisible waves from the sun that are warm and are part of the spectrum of light (electro-magnetic waves).

molecules – groups of atoms that make distinct compounds that, in turn, are the building blocks of all things.

nutrients – basic molecules that contain elements to help an organism, including a tree, use energy to grow and sustain itself.

organic – any molecule that contains the element carbon and is part of a living thing. We get the word *organism* from this word.

Periodic Table (of Elements) – an organized chart that lists the most basic atoms that make up the molecules of everything on earth. Each are unique with special properties.

photosynthesis – a process in which plants use the sun's energy and molecules from the earth and atmosphere to live and grow.

pressure – in our story, it is the pull of gravity on molecules in the atmosphere to bring them closer together. The pull of gravity is weaker the farther you are from the center of the earth (the higher you get), so the air molecules move farther apart. These air molecules that are farther apart makes bags sealed at sea level expand as you climb higher into the mountains.

sapwood – the wood just under the living cambium layer that helps transport water and nutrients throughout a tree.

stoma – special openings on the underside of leaves that can open and close, allowing molecules in and out.

Tharp, Hale – a 19th-century cattleman who made his home in a fallen Giant Sequoia log in Crescent Meadow, Sequoia National Park.

About the Author and Artists

Nancy Muleady-Mecham
A professor of biology and retired Park Ranger, Nancy is the author of several books. This is her first children's book. As a naturalist, she has made a career of bringing the wonder and science of the outdoor world to audiences around the globe. She lives in the Sierra Nevada mountains with her husband, Kent.

Robert E. Muleady
A professional illustrator and cartoonist, Robert has edited and contributed to scores of media in his career. He has wanted to be a cartoonist ever since he could remember. Robert uses markers and colored pencils for his drawings. He lives in California with his wife, Sandra, and two sons, Sean and Daniel.

Sandra Kim Muleady
A graphic artist who has freelanced for The Huntington Library and various Disney projects, Sandra has designed many books and other media. She lives in California with her husband, Robert, and two sons, Sean and Daniel.

Other Books by the Author for the Older Crowd

PARK RANGER:
True Stories from a Ranger's Career in America's National Parks

PARK RANGER Sequel:
More True Stories from a Ranger's Career in America's National Parks